JOHN AGARD is one of the most popular poets
writing in Britain today. His collection of poetry for young children,
We Animals Would Like a Word With You, was shortlisted for the
Nestle Children's Book Prize and he is the author of the well-loved
Brer Rabbit and the Tug of War, illustrated by Korky Paul.
He has written *Butter-Finger* and *Shine On, Butter-Finger* for Frances Lincoln.
John lives in Brighton.

JENNY BENT's family lived in Jamaica,
but she now has her home near London. Jenny began working as an illustrator
after graduating from Harrow Art College. She also teaches art classes.
Her first book was *Calypso Alphabet*, written by John Agard.
This was followed by *The Green Banana Hunt* and *How Anansi Captured the Tiger*,
which she both wrote and illustrated.
Wriggle Piggy Toes is her first book for Frances Lincoln.

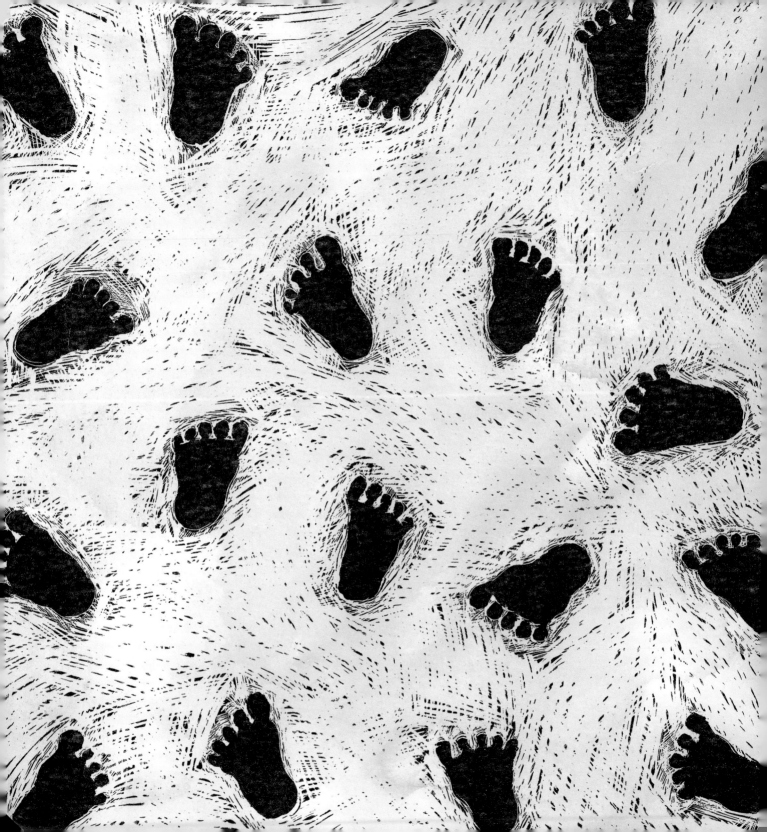

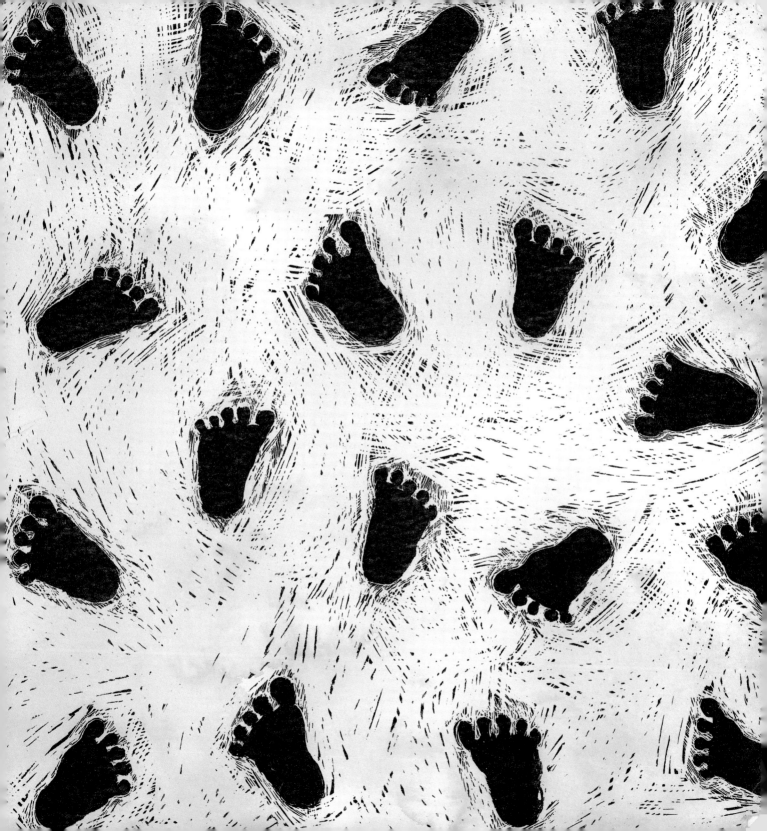

In loving memory of my mother and father – J.B.

First published in Great Britain and in the USA in 2005 by
Frances Lincoln Children's Books, 4 Torriano Mews,
Torriano Avenue, London NW5 2RZ
www.franceslincoln.com

First paperback edition published in Great Britain in 2008

British Library Cataloguing in Publication Data available on request

ISBN: 978-1-84507-486-9

Printed in China

1 3 5 7 9 8 6 4 2

Wriggle Piggy Toes

John Agard
Illustrated by Jenny Bent

F
FRANCES LINCOLN
CHILDREN'S BOOKS

Wakey light, wakey light,
creeping through window.
Now open peepy eyes.
Now wriggle piggy toes.

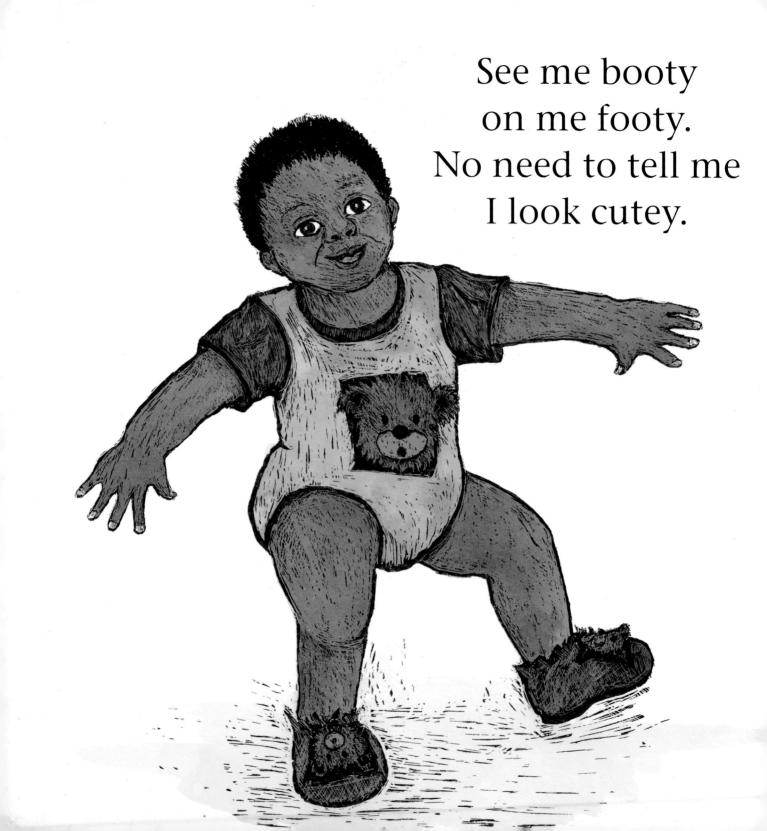

See me booty
on me footy.
No need to tell me
I look cutey.

Dribble goes out.
Mushy goes in.
Long as I have my bib
under my chin.

One day I'll sit botty
on what they call potty.
Now I do in cotty
what I call a dotty.

I like to pull-pull
Daddy chin-hair.
More fun than playing
with teddy bear.

Wish I was a whale,
I'd tipple my tail.
Wish I was a whale,
I'd topple that scale.

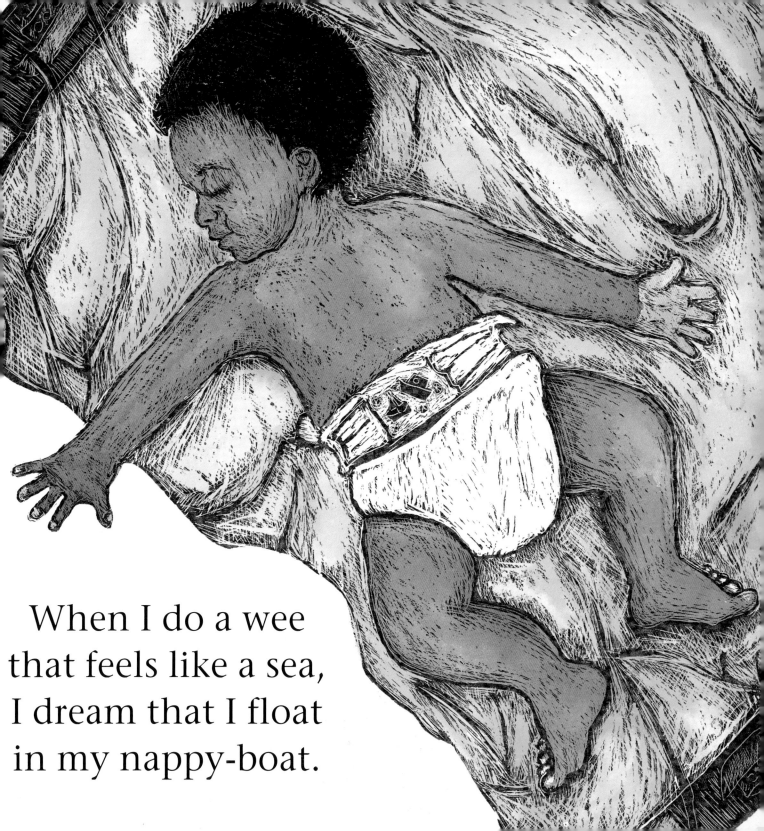

When I do a wee
that feels like a sea,
I dream that I float
in my nappy-boat.

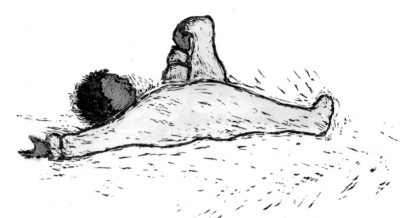

Finger and toe
are good to suck
but I prefer
my rubber duck.

Mummy's earrings
are little swings.
I love to pull them
when she sings.

Moon-ball, Moon-ball,
you shine so bright.
Eye-ball, Eye-ball,
time to sleep tight.

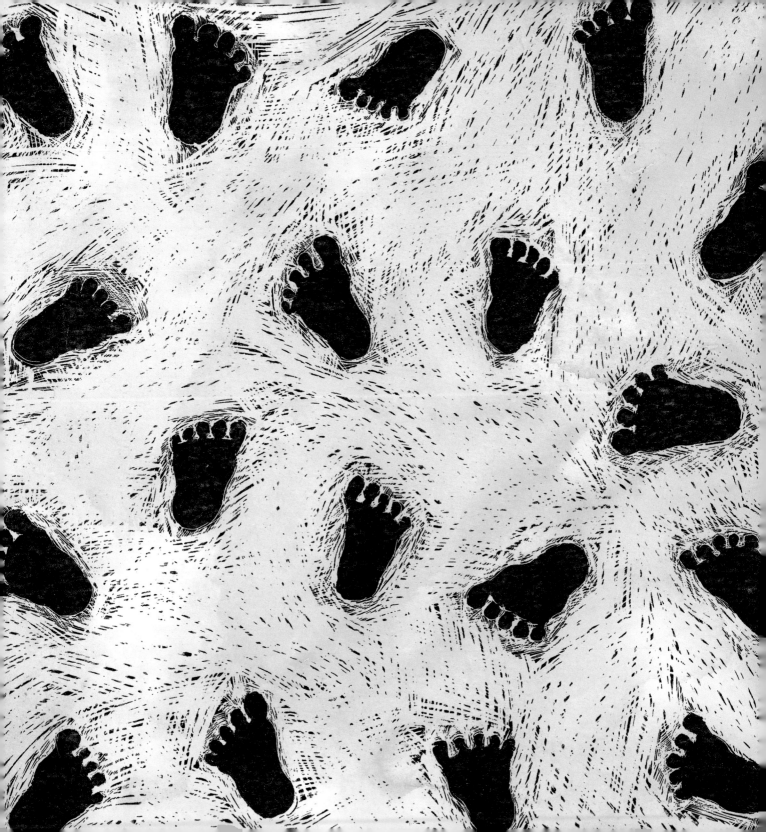

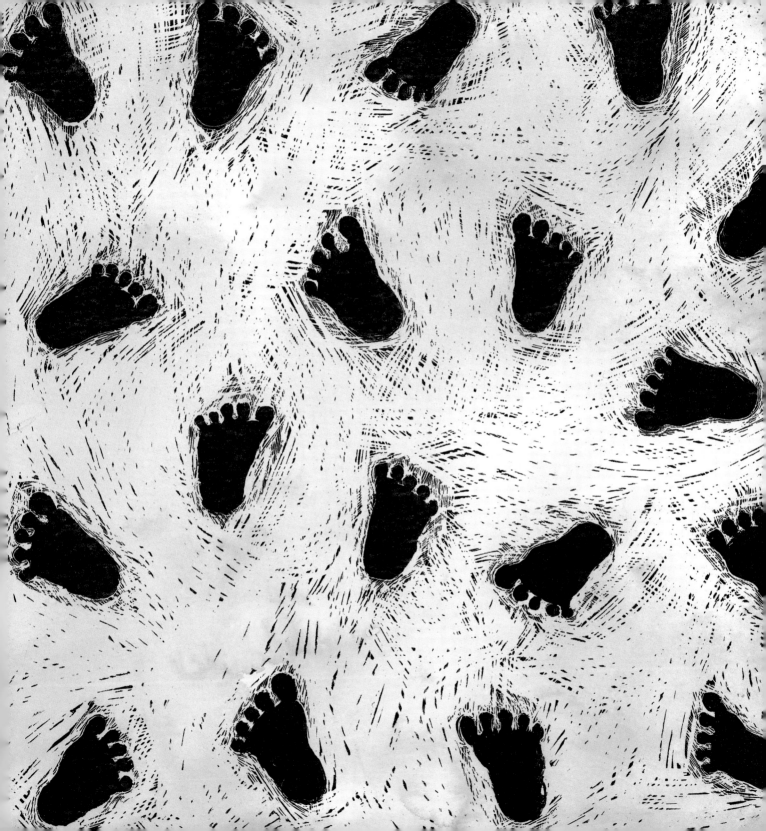

MORE TITLES FROM FRANCES LINCOLN CHILDREN'S BOOKS

Hippety-hop, Hippety-hay
Growing with rhymes from birth to age 3
Opal Dunn
Illustrated by Sally Anne Lambert

In *Hippety-hop, Hippety-hay*, language consultant Opal Dunn includes rhymes appropriate to each stage of development from birth to age 3, and gives practical advice on how to say rhymes as well as actions to accompany them, games to play, and music for songs.

ISBN 978-0-7112-1195-7

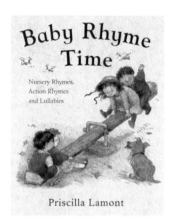

Baby Rhyme Time
Priscilla Lamont

A wealth of traditional rhymes to listen to, action rhymes to clap and dance to, and lullabies complete with music. Here is a book brimming with opportunities for babies, toddlers and parents to have fun together.

ISBN 978-1-84507-714-3

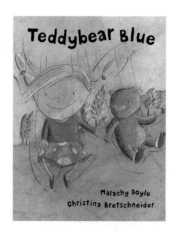

Teddybear Blue
Malachy Doyle
Illustrated by Christina Bretschneider

Teddybear Blue is always disappearing!
His owner wants to cuddle him but he's run off to play hide-and-seek, or he's in a cupboard, or he's in the park. Yet, however good or bad he may be, no toy is as special as Teddybear Blue.

ISBN 978-1-84507-126-4